W9-BMV-530

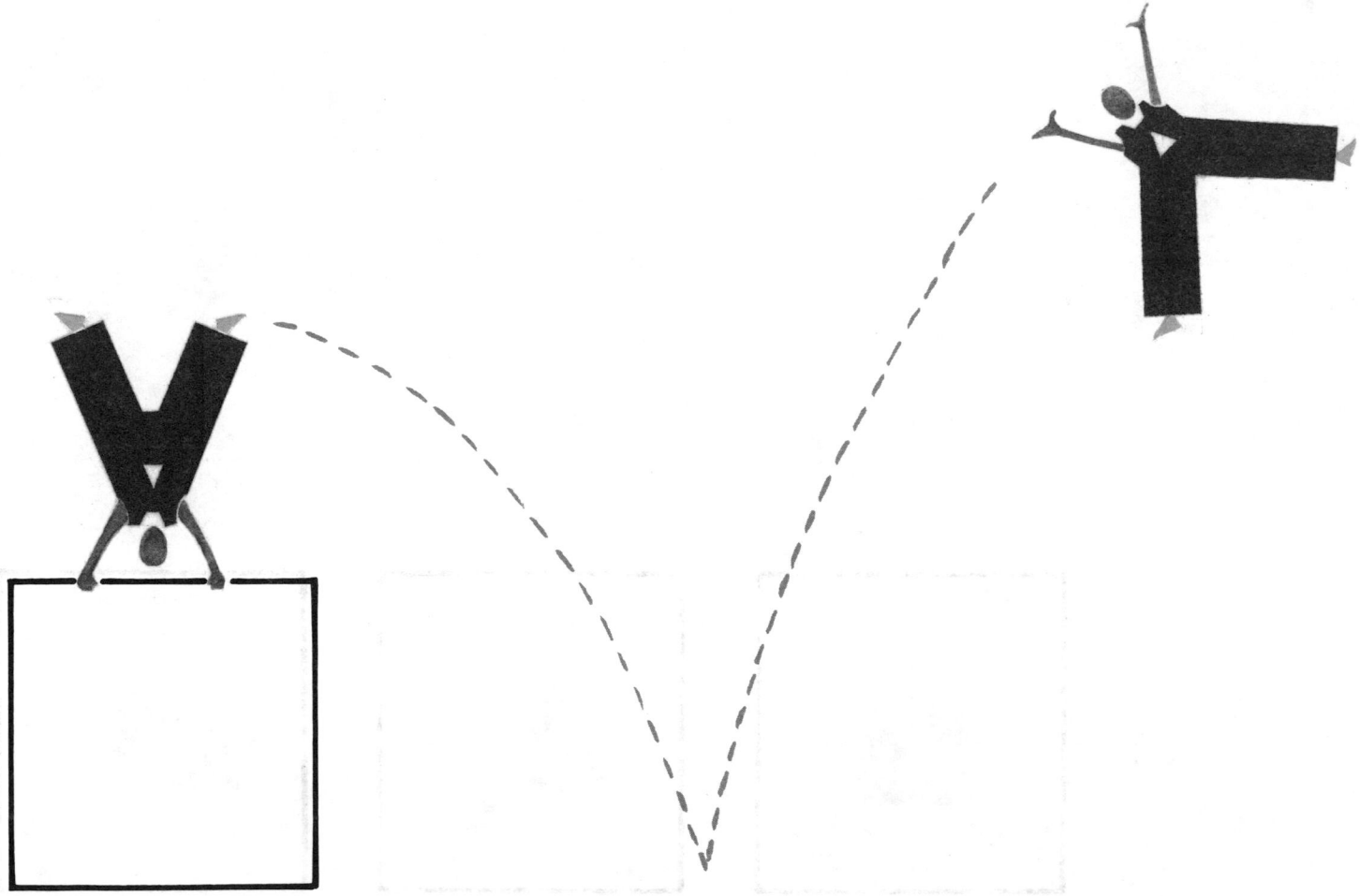

ALPHABATICS

Suse MacDonald

A TRUMPET CLUB SPECIAL EDITION

Aa

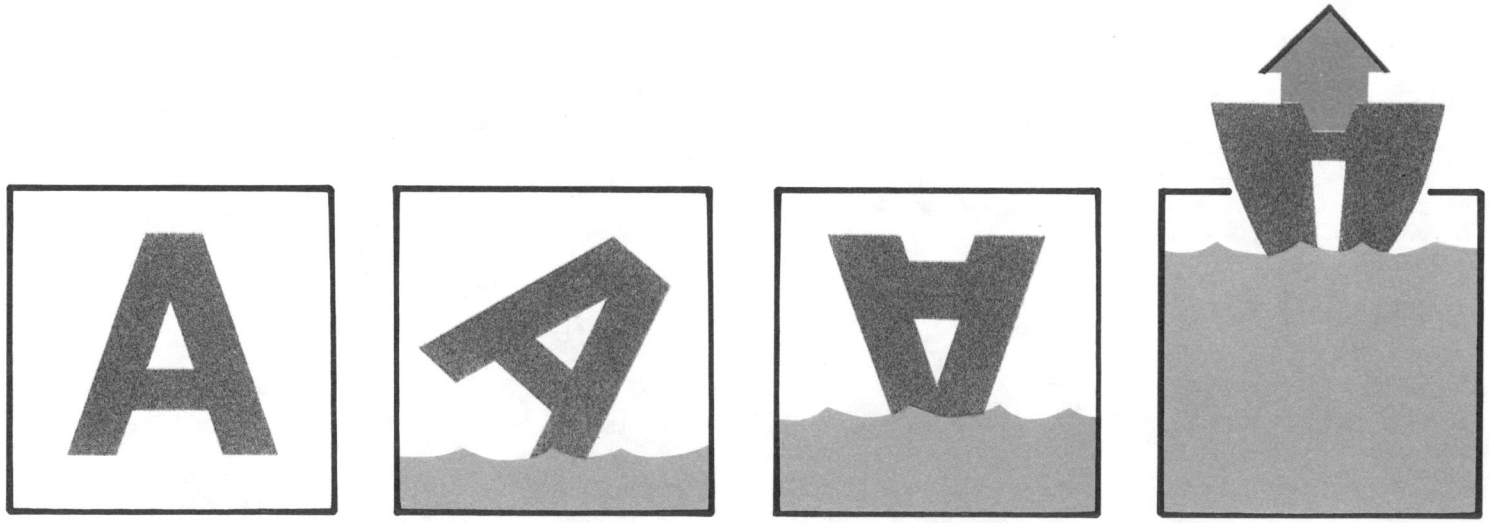

Ark

Bb

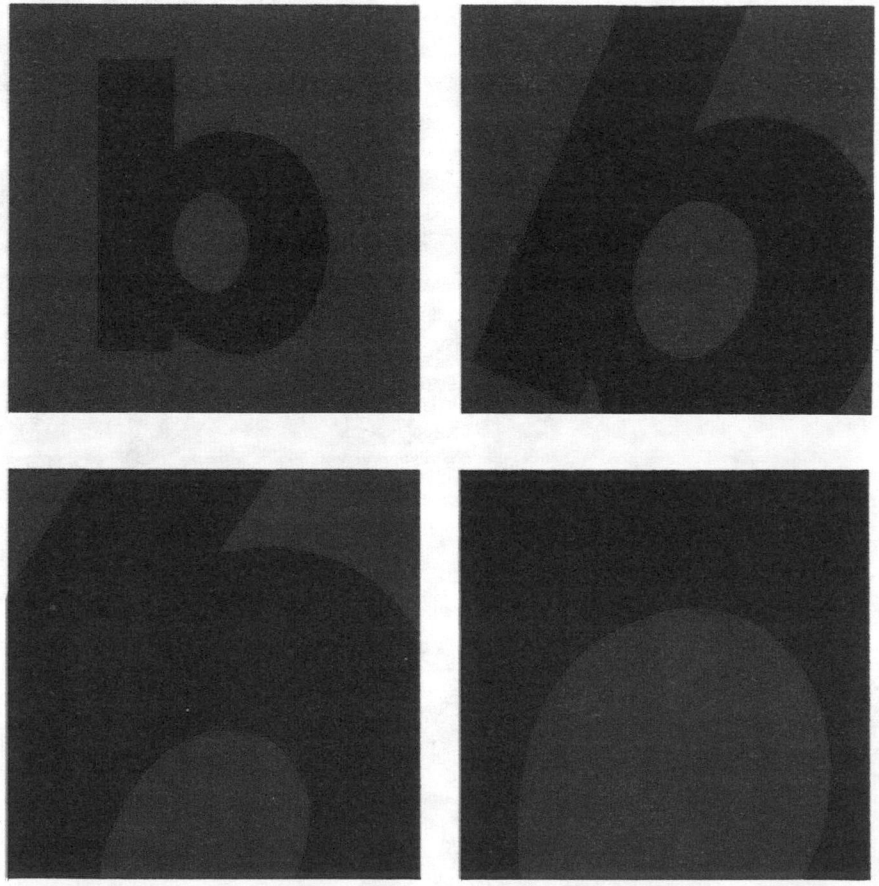

balloon

Cc

Clown

Dd

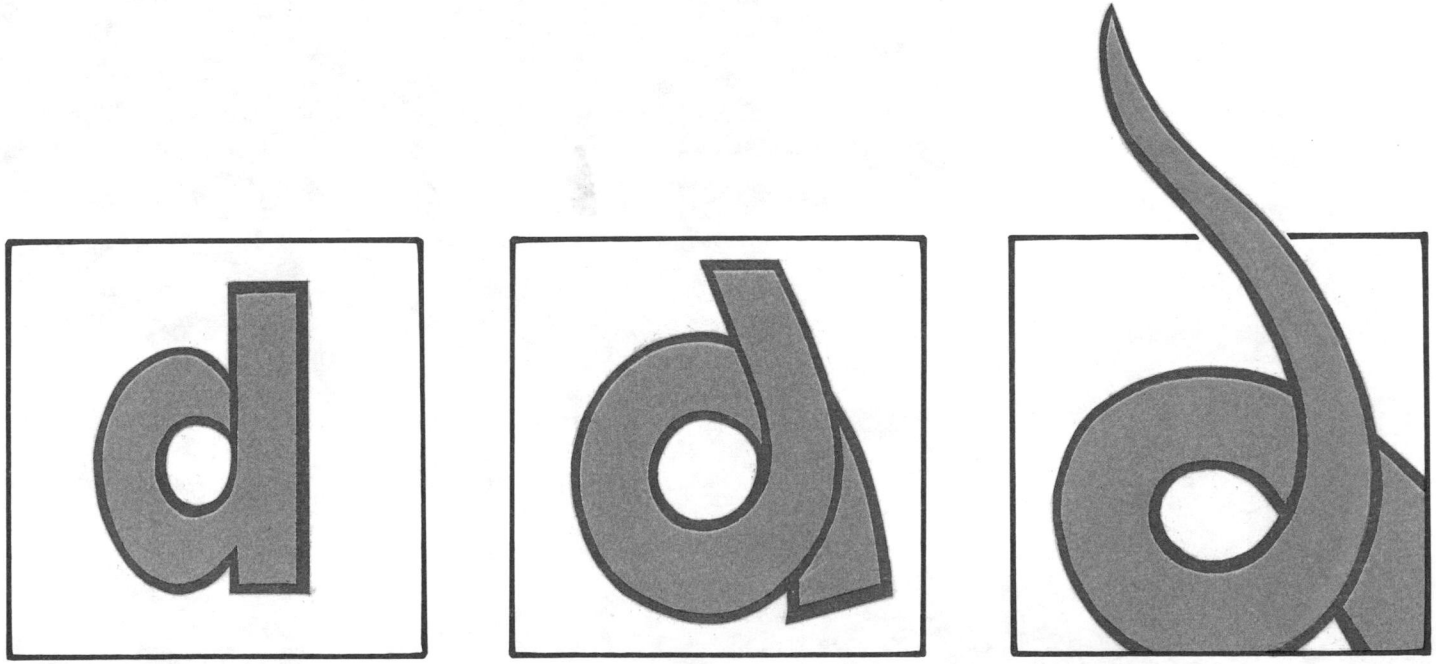

dragon

Ee

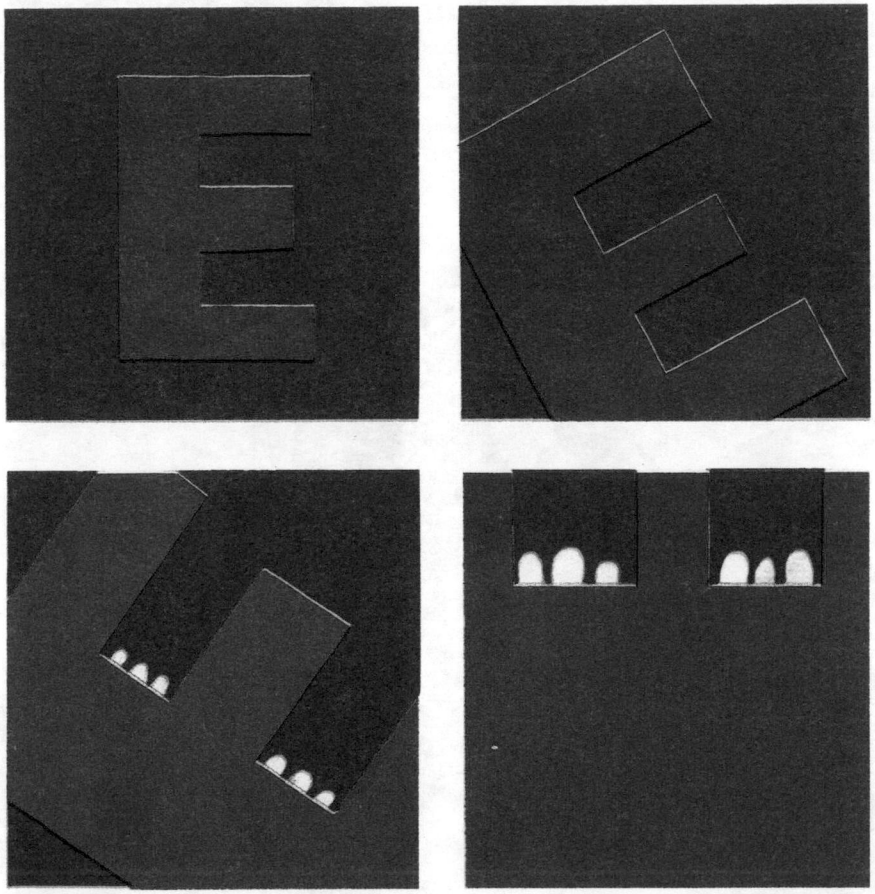

Elephant

Ff

Fish

Gg

Giraffe

Hh

house

insect

Jj

jack-in-the-box

Kk

Kite

Lion

Mm

mustache

Nn

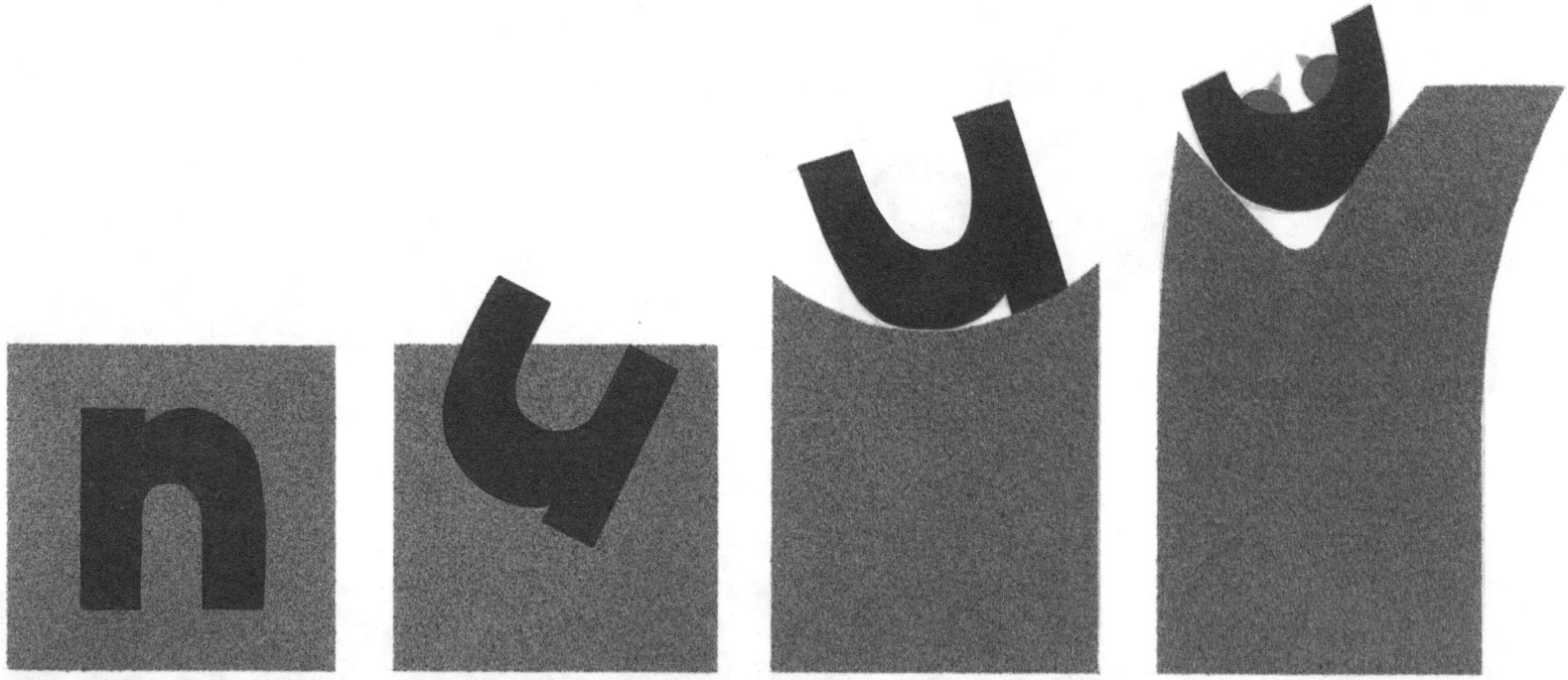

nest

Oo

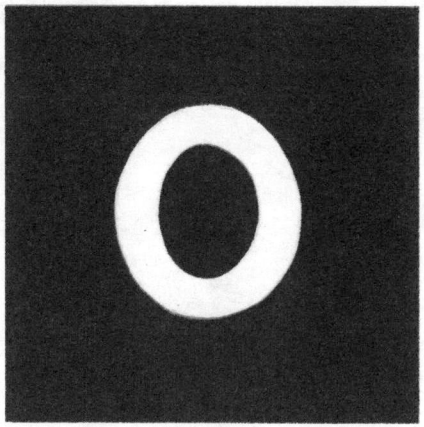

owl

Pp
P

Plane

Qq

Quail

Rr

rooster

Ss

Swan

Tt

Tree

Uu

umbrella

Vv

Vegetables

Ww

Whale

Xx

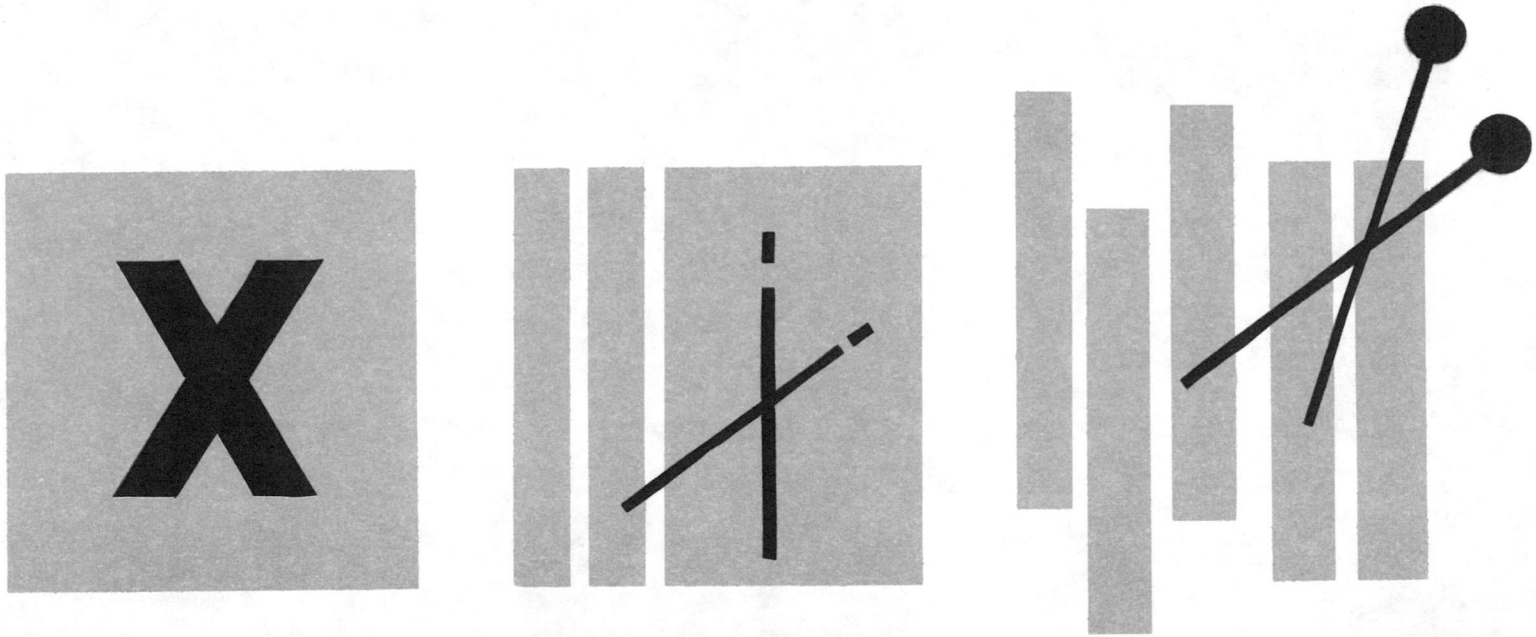

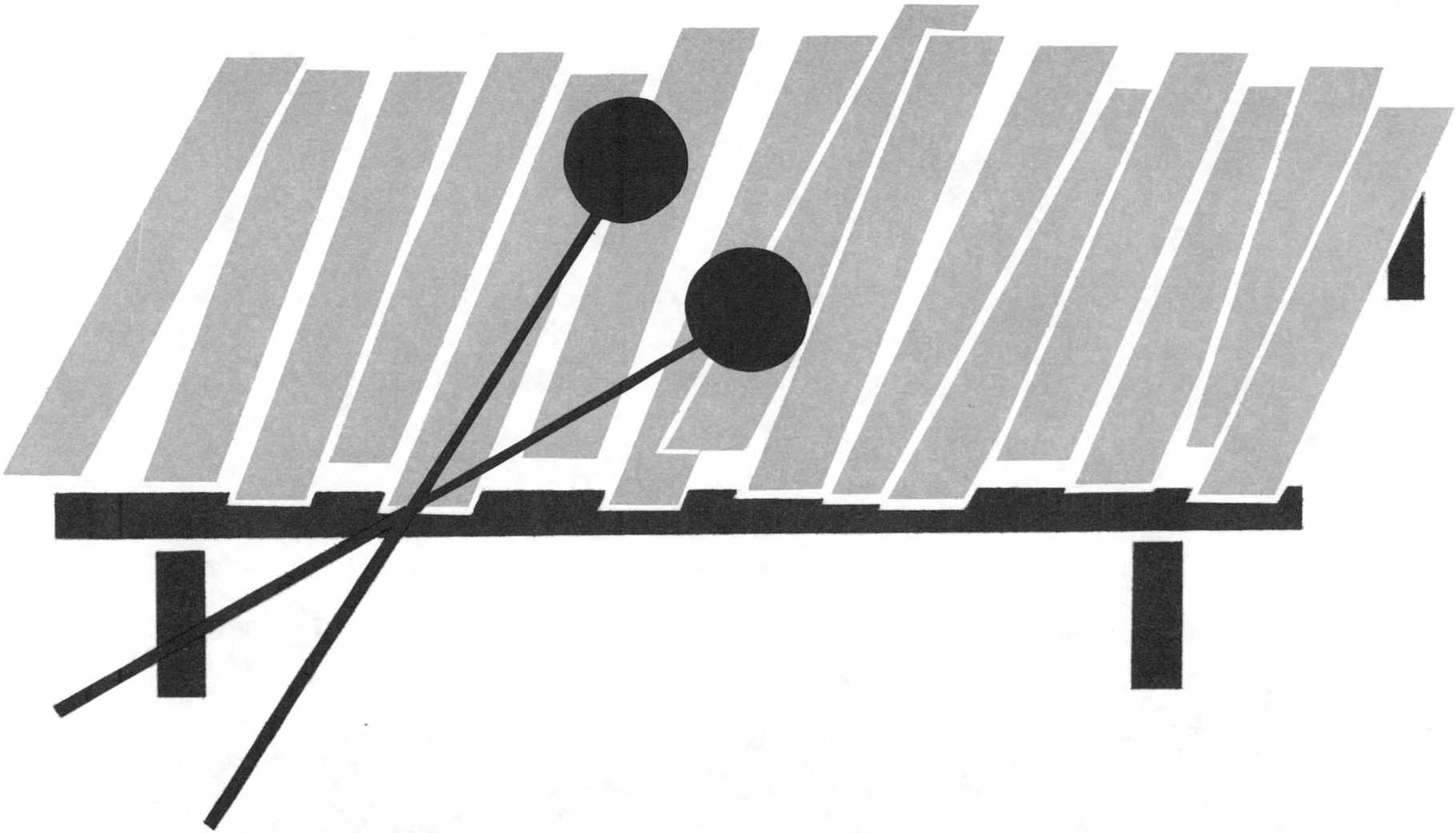

Xylophone

Yy

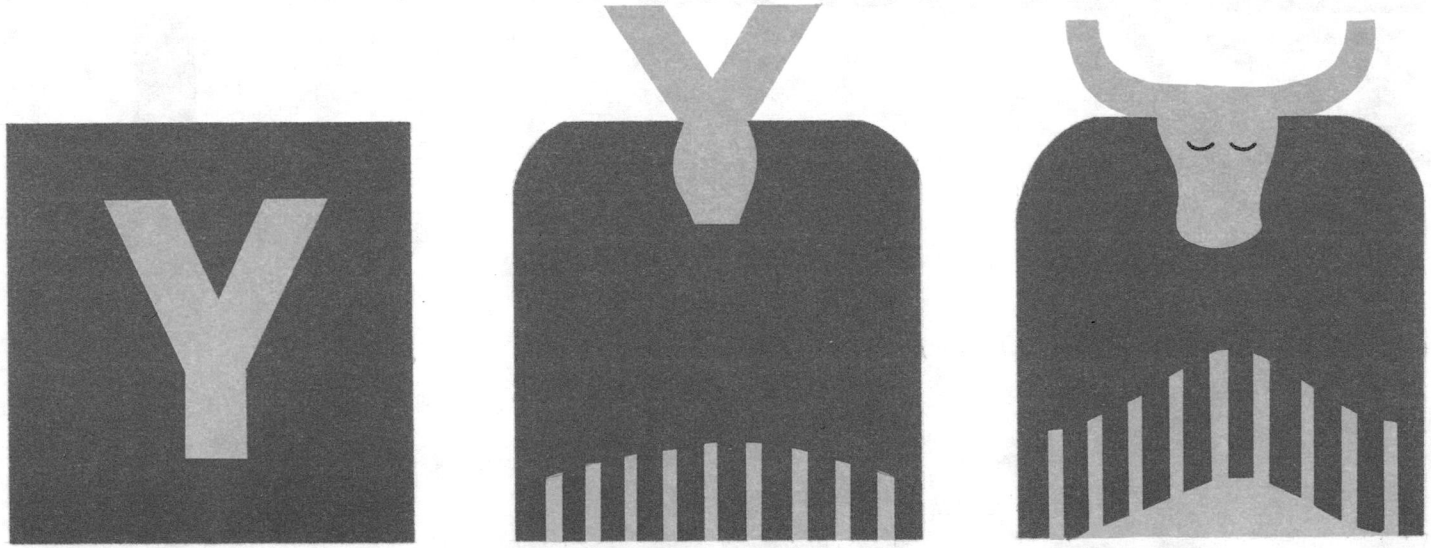

Yak

Zz

Zebra

For Stuart, with special thanks to Susan and Deborah

Published by The Trumpet Club, 666 Fifth Avenue, New York, New York 10103

Copyright © 1986 by Suse MacDonald

All rights reserved. No part of this book may be reproduced or transmitted in any form or by any means, electronic or mechanical, including photocopying, recording or by any information storage and retrieval system, without the written permission of the Publisher, except where permitted by law. For information address: Bradbury Press, an affiliate of Macmillan Publishing Company, New York, New York.

ISBN: 0-440-84473-8

This edition published by arrangement with Bradbury Press, an affiliate of Macmillan Publishing Company
Printed in the United States of America October 1991

10 9 8 7 6 5 4 3 2 1
UPC